Alphabet

Aa Bb Cc Dd Ee Ff

Gg Hh Ii Jj Kk Ll

Mm Nn Oo Pp Qq Rr

Ss Tt Uu Vv Ww Xx

Yy Zz

Let's Trace the Letter

To Parents: Have your child trace the dotted line with a crayon or pencil multiple times. Guide your child to follow the writing order of each line of the letter.

2

Month	Day	Name
10	29	

Good Job!

Trace ----- to draw the uppercase letter A. Then, place apple stickers in the tree away from the hungry ants.

ant   apple

Let's Name the Animal

To Parents: Remind your child of the shape of the letter B if he or she has trouble determining which areas to color. When your child is finished coloring, a bear appears. Help your child name other B words in the picture.

3

Month	Day	Name
10	29	

Good Job!

Color the areas with the uppercase letter B. Name what you see.

 bear bee

Let's Make a Cat

To Parents: Read the instructions for your child as he or she draws the cat. Creating a melody to sing the instructions will help encourage your child to draw.

4

Month	Day	Name
10	29	

Good Job!

Trace the uppercase letter C. Then, draw the face of a cat using a crayon.

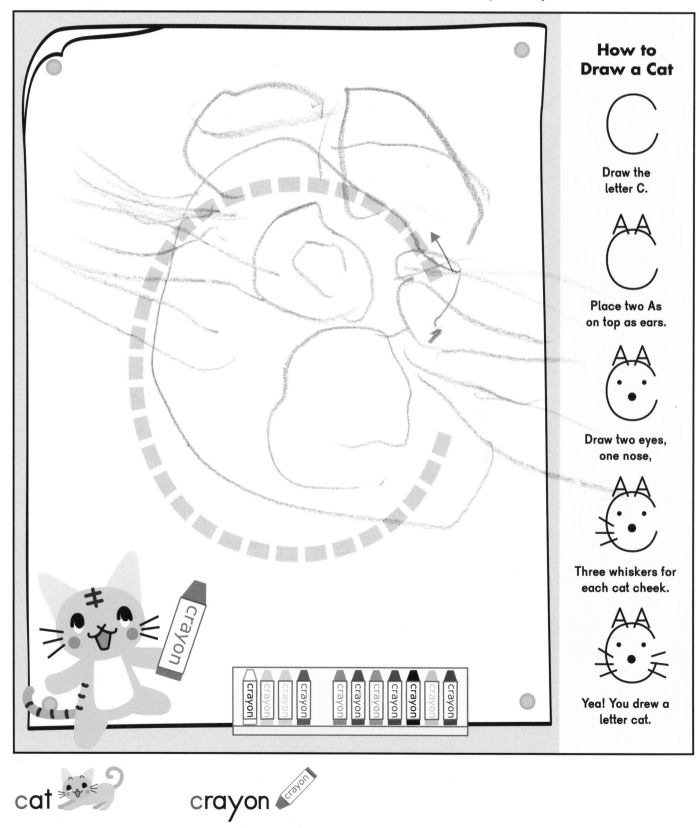

How to Draw a Cat

C
Draw the letter C.

AA
Place two As on top as ears.

Draw two eyes, one nose,

Three whiskers for each cat cheek.

Yea! You drew a letter cat.

cat   crayon

Let's Follow the Path

To Parents: If your child has difficulty folding the page, guide him or her to fold the page according to the directions. When your child folds the page, an uppercase letter D should appear.

5

Month	Day	Name

Good Job!

Draw a line from ➡ to ➡ to get the dog from his house to the doughnut.
Name what you see when you fold --- line and — – — line.

- - - - - Fold up
—·—·— Fold down

How To Fold

Fold

Fold

 dog    doughnut

Let's Write Letters

To Parents: Let your child write each uppercase and lowercase letter repeatedly to help with spatial recognition of each letter form.

Good Job!

Month	Day	Name

Trace the letters A, a, B, b following the number order.

apple

ant

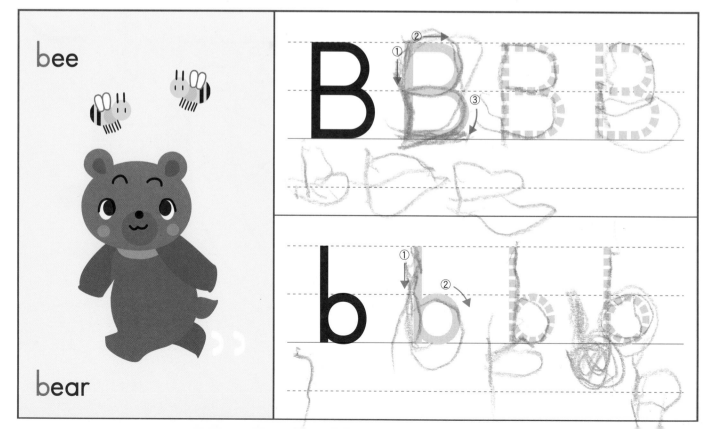

bee

bear

Let's Write Letters

To Parents: Some children have difficulty distinguishing between the lowercase letters b and d. Point out the similarities and differences to your child.

7

Month	Day	Name
		1/30/13

Good Job!

Trace the letters C, c, D, d following the number order.

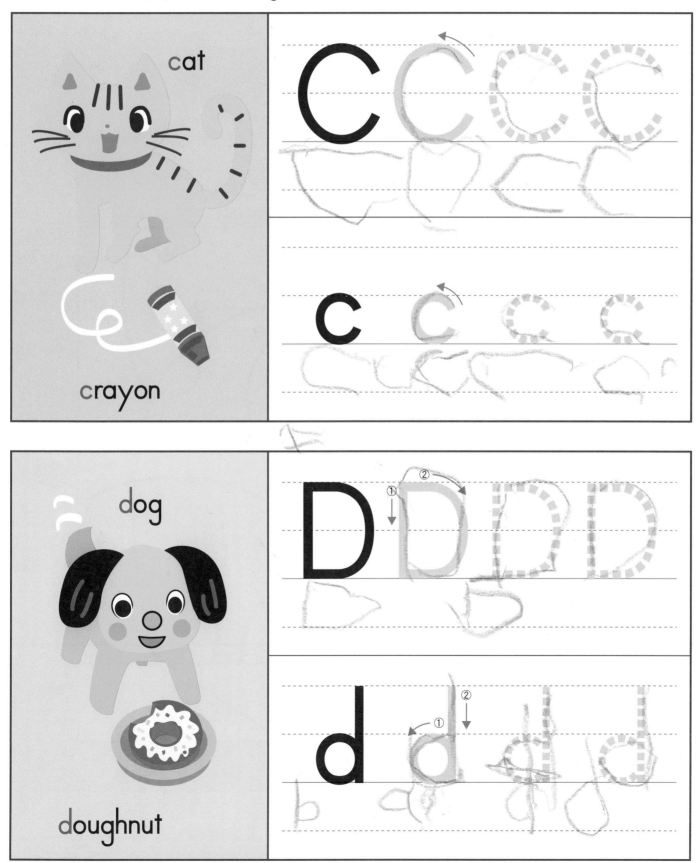

cat

crayon

dog

doughnut

Let's Name the Animal

To Parents: Remind your child of the shape of the letter E if he or she has trouble determining which areas to color. When your child is finished coloring, an elephant appears. Ask your child to name what the elephant is holding (egg).

8

Month	Day	Name

Good Job!

Color the areas with the uppercase letter E. Name what you see.
Place the egg sticker to finish the picture.

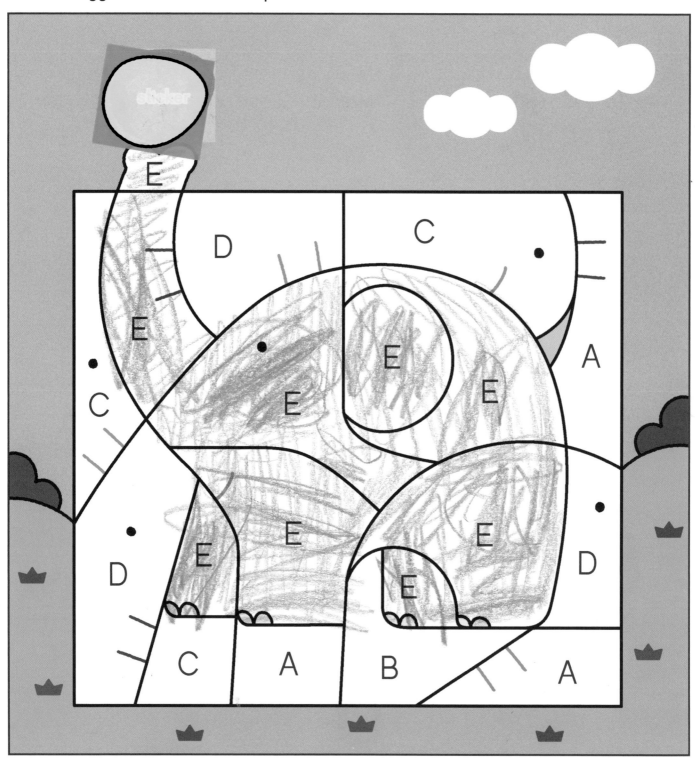

elephant    egg ◯

To Parents: When your child places the frog sticker, say, "Frog starts with the letter F."

Let's Follow the Path

Month	Day	Name

Good Job!

Draw a line from ➡ to ➡ to help the frog find its way. Find a way without any fish.
Place frog stickers on each uppercase letter F in the path.

 frog

 fish

Let's Finish the Picture

Month	Day	Name

Good Job!

Find the uppercase letter G's and draw ◯ around each. Then, place stickers for the goat's eyes and nose. Color the goat and grapes to finish the picture.

goat   grape(s)

Let's Make a House

Month	Day	Name

Trace the uppercase letter H.
Then, draw a picture of a house around the girl wearing the hat.

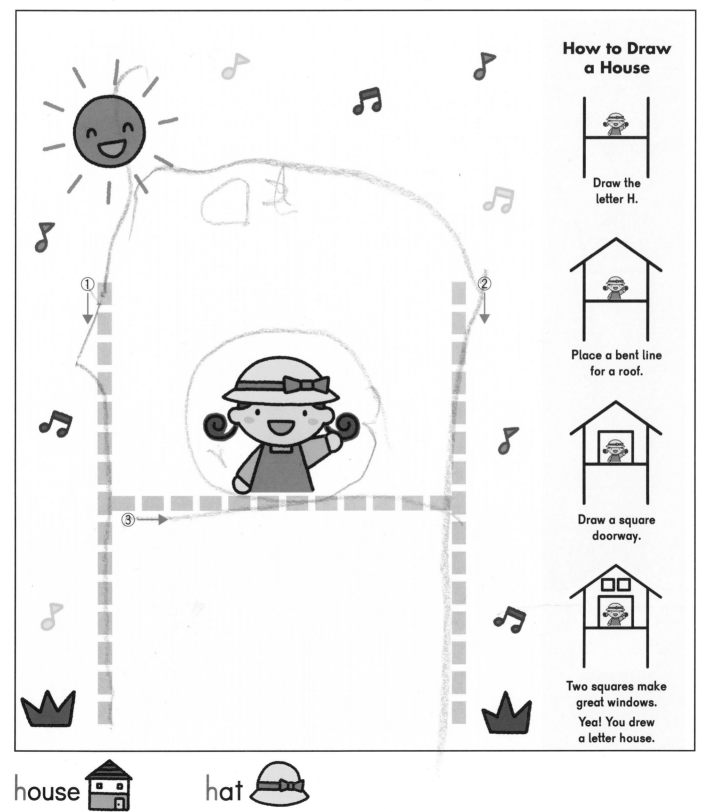

How to Draw a House

Draw the letter H.

Place a bent line for a roof.

Draw a square doorway.

Two squares make great windows.
Yea! You drew a letter house.

house   hat

Let's Follow the Path

Month	Day	Name

Draw a line from ➡ to ➡ by finding the path of letter I's. Color the two Ⅱ's, and then place the stickers to finish the ice cream sundae.

G F I I
I D B
I C
sticker

ice cream

Let's Follow the Path

Month	Day	Name

Help the witch through the jack-o'-lantern. Draw a line from ➡ to ➡ by finding the path marked by the letter J. When you find the letter J, say it out loud.

juice

jack-o-lantern

Let's Write Letters

To Parents: Encourage your child to follow the numbers in order for proper handwriting, but the most important idea is that he or she recognizes the shapes of the letters and can write them.

Month	Day	Name

Good Job!

Good Job Sticker

Trace the letters E, e, F, f, G, g following the number order.

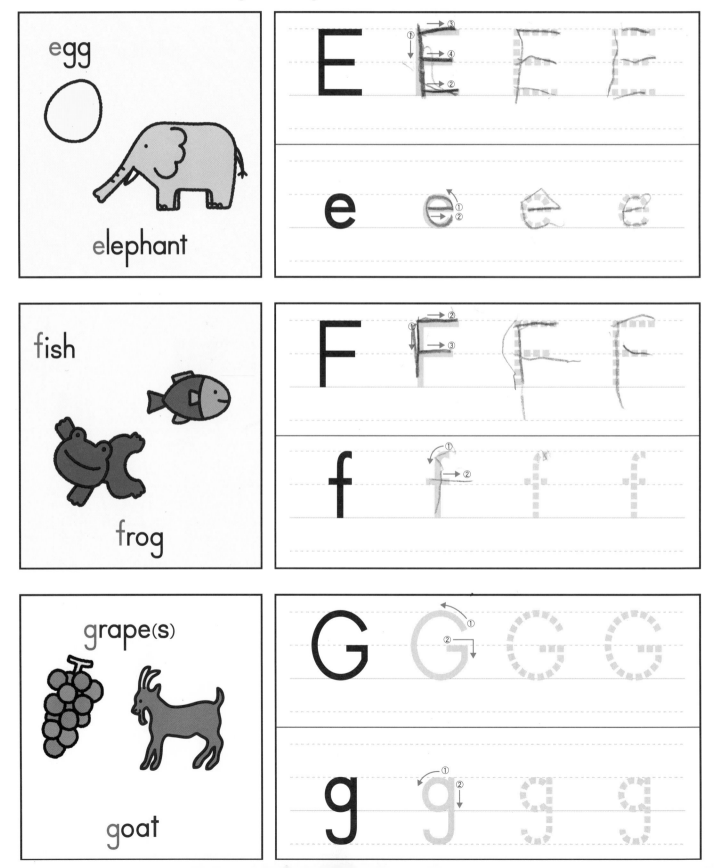

egg

elephant

fish

frog

grape(s)

goat

Let's Write Letters

To Parents: Make sure your child traces the top and bottom bars on the uppercase letter I.

Month	Day	Name

Good Job!

Good Job Sticker

Trace the letters H, h, I, i, J, j following the number order.

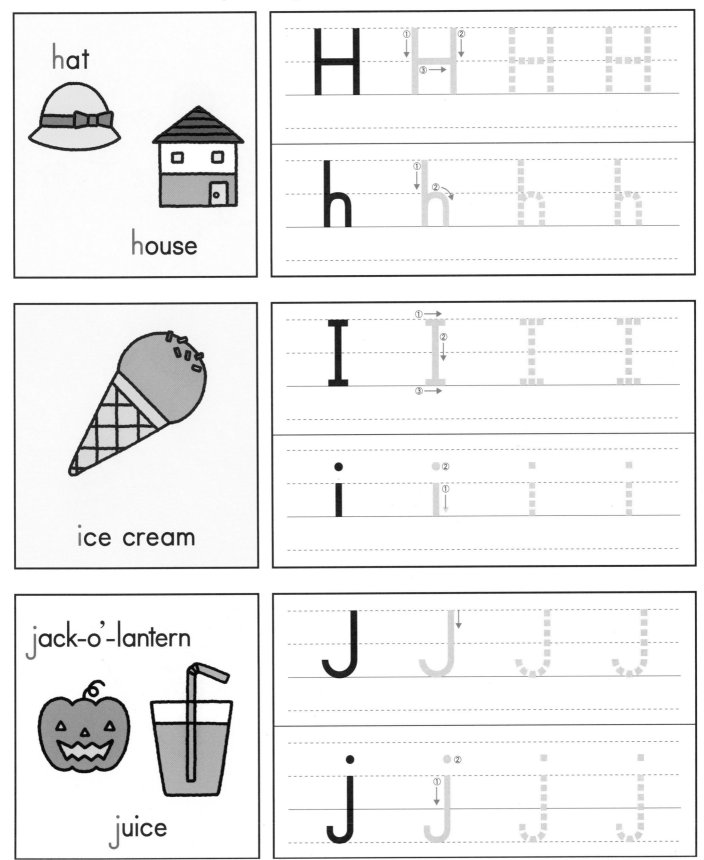

hat

house

ice cream

jack-o'-lantern

juice

Let's Finish the Picture

Month	Day	Name

Good Job!

Good Job Sticker

Find the three letter Ks and draw ◯ around each.
Then, draw eyebrows and a mustache on the king's face.

Example

king   key

Let's Finish the Picture

To Parents: After your child connects the dots, a lion should appear.

17

Month	Day	Name

Good Job!
Good Job Sticker

Connect the dots in ABC order. Name the animal that has a sour face after eating a lemon.

lion   lemon

Let's Trace the Letter

Month	Day	Name

Trace each letter M following the number order. Then, help the monkeys eat.
Place a banana in each monkey's mouth. Color each monkey with your favorite colors.

monkey

Let's Follow the Path

Month	Day	Name

Color each nut that has the uppercase letter N. Then, draw a line from ➡ to ➡ to help the squirrel gather nuts in the maze.

nut

Let's Finish the Picture

Month	Day	Name

Good Job!

Good Job Sticker

Find all of the uppercase letter Os and color them.

 octopus

Let's Follow the Path

Good Job!

Good Job Sticker

Draw a line from ➡ to ➡ to get the penguin to his friends. Place the hat stickers with the uppercase letter P on each penguin's head.

penguin

Let's Write Letters

To Parents: Uppercase letter M can be written in the order: 1, 3, 4, 2, too.

22

Month	Day	Name

Good Job!

Good Job
Sticker

Trace the letters K, k, L, l, M, m following the number order.

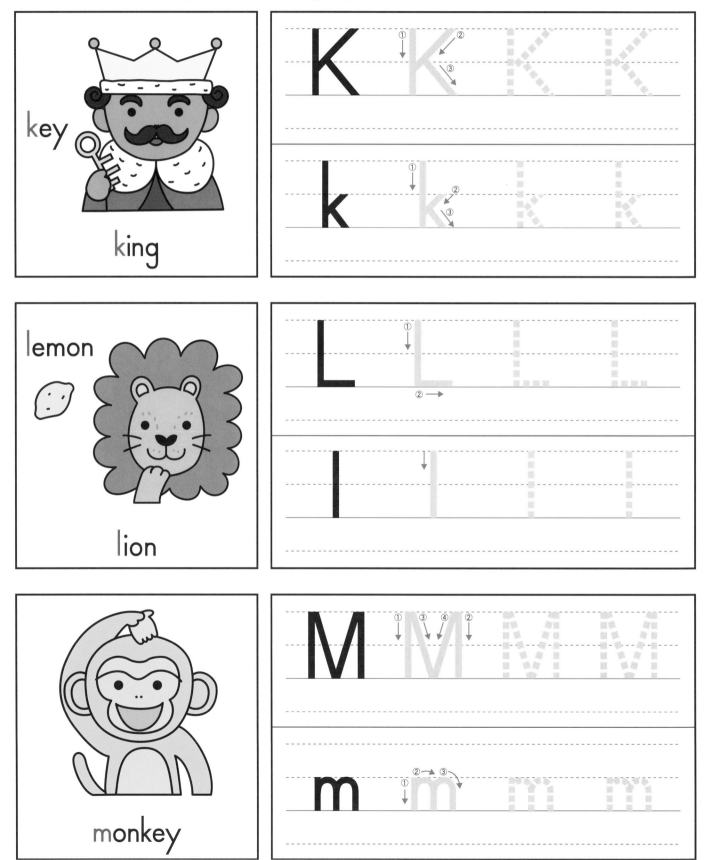

key

king

lemon

lion

monkey

Let's Write Letters

To Parents: Uppercase letter N can be written in the order: 1, 3, 2, too.

23

Month	Day	Name

Good Job!

Good Job
Sticker

Trace the letters N, n, O, o, P, p following the number order.

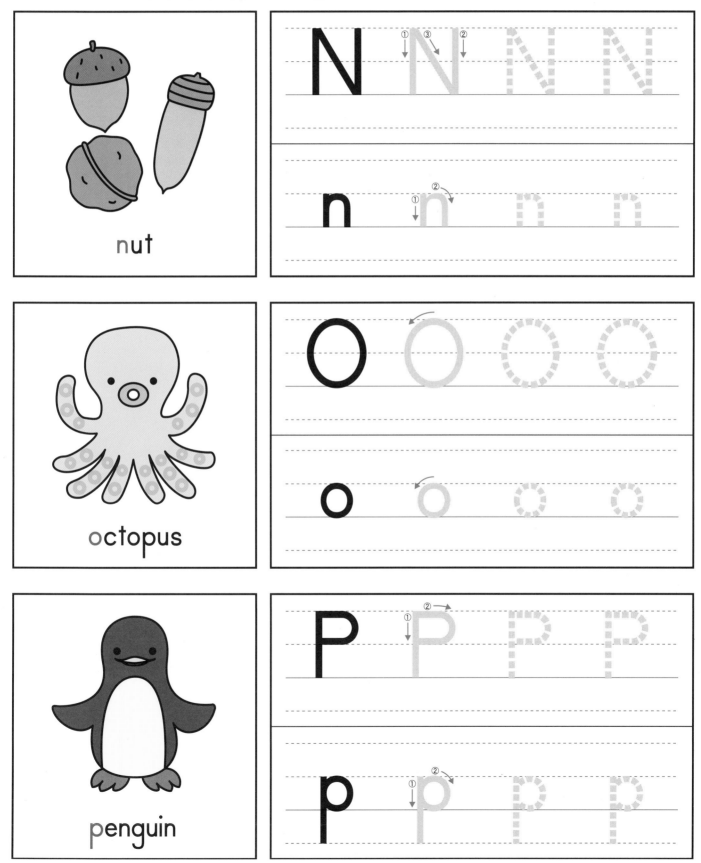

nut

octopus

penguin

Let's Color the Letter

To Parents: After your child colors the areas with gray hearts, an uppercase letter Q should appear.

24

Month	Day	Name

Good Job!

Good Job Sticker

Color in red only areas with ♥ to see what letter appears on the queen's dress.

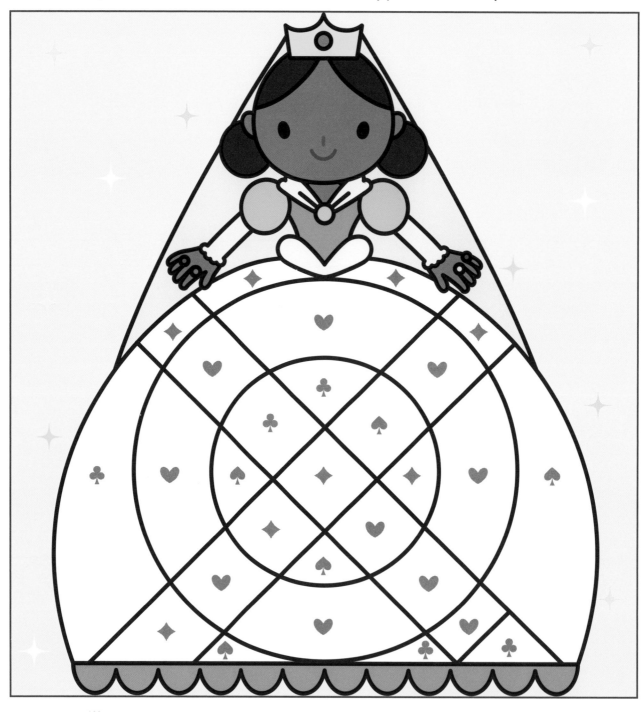

queen

Let's Trace the Path

Month	Day	Name

Find all the planets that have an uppercase letter R. Then, place rabbit stickers on the planets. Trace the ▬ ▬ ▬ to show the rocket's path from ➡ to ➡.

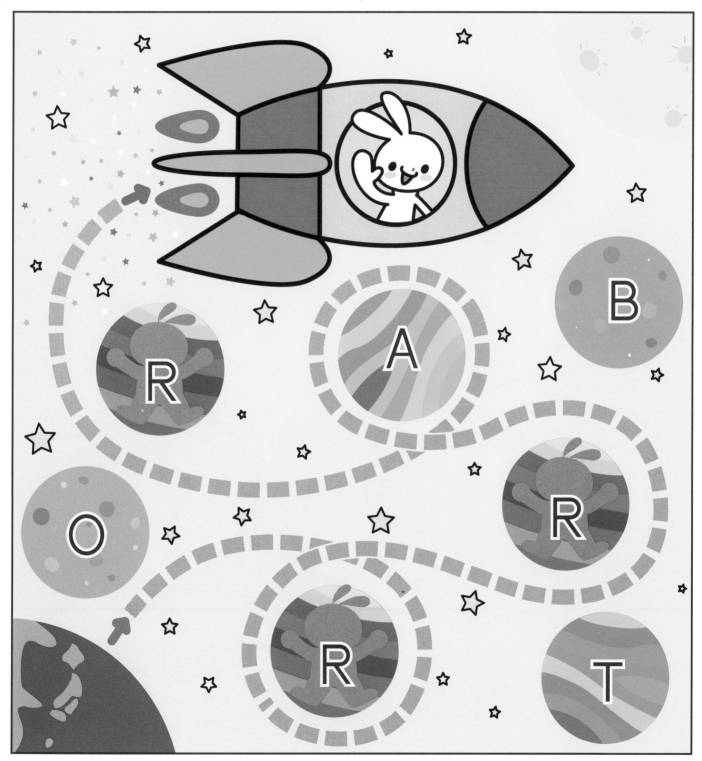

rocket

rabbit

Let's Trace the Letter

Month	Day	Name

Trace the ---- from ➡ to ➡. You just traced an uppercase and lowercase letter S. Place the snake face stickers on each letter S snake.

snake

Let's Follow the Path

Month	Day	Name

Draw a line from ➡ to ➡ by going through the tiger's stripes. Find the uppercase letter T in the picture. Draw ◯ around it.

tiger

Let's Choose the Letters

Month	Day	Name

Find the uppercase letter U on each of the 3 umbrellas.
Color each letter U with your favorite colors.

umbrella

Let's Finish the Picture

To Parents: After your child connects the dots, a violin should appear.

Month	Day	Name

Good Job!

Good Job Sticker

Connect the dots in ABC order from letter A through V.
Name the instrument the giraffe is playing.

violin

Let's Write Letters

Month	Day	Name

Good Job!

Good Job
Sticker

Trace the letters Q, q, R, r, S, s following the number order.

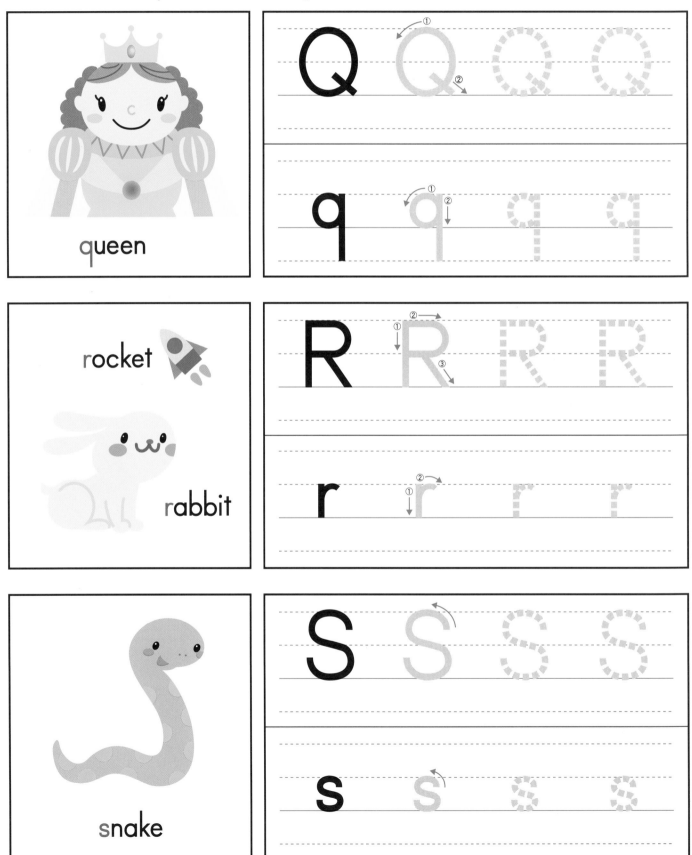

queen

rocket

rabbit

snake

Let's Write Letters

To Parents: Point out the differences in the often-confused letters of U and V. (The bottom of the uppercase letter U is round, and the V is pointed). Note that the uppercase letter U can be written with one stroke instead of two.

Month	Day	Name

Good Job!

Good Job Sticker

Trace the letters T, t, U, u, V, v following the number order.

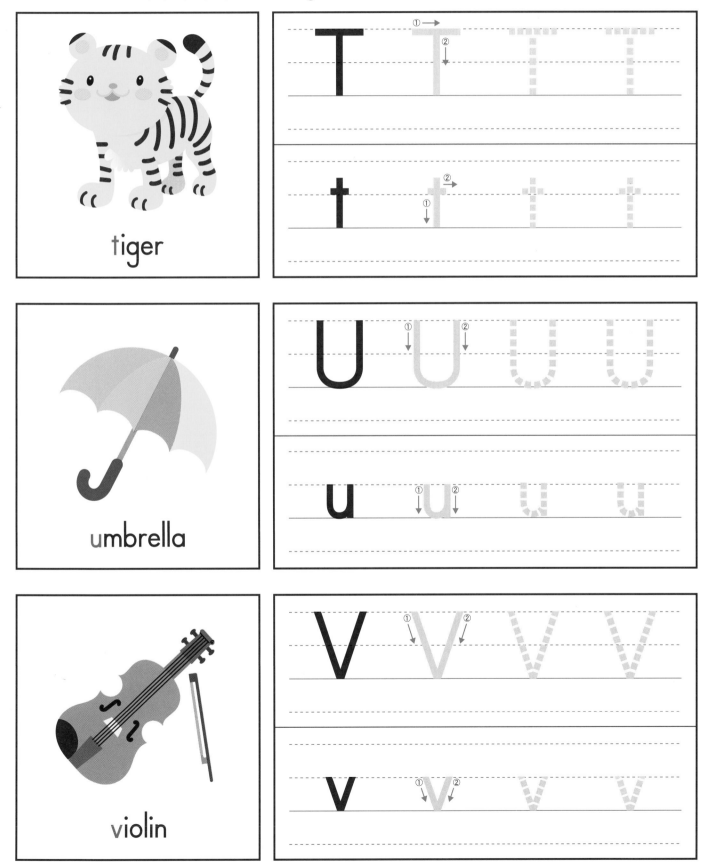

tiger

umbrella

violin

Let's Follow the Path

To Parents: Encourage your child to follow the numbers in order for proper handwriting, but the most important idea is that he or she recognizes the shapes of the letters and can write them.

Month	Day	Name

Draw a line from ➡ to ➡ to get through the water maze.
Trace the uppercase letter W on the whale.

① ② ③ ④

whale

Let's Follow the Path

To Parents: It is less common for your child to see words that start with the letter X, so this activity uses words that end with the letter X.

Month	Day	Name

Good Job!

Good Job
Sticker

Find the boxes with the uppercase letter Xs. Place the fox stickers on them.

Then, draw a line from ➡ to ➡ to help the fox through the maze.

Example

fox   box

Let's Color the Letter

To Parents: After your child colors the areas with the pink stars, an uppercase letter Y should appear.

34

Month	Day	Name

Good Job!

Good Job Sticker

Color only the areas with ⭐ to see what letter appears on the sail of the yacht.

 yacht

Let's Follow the Path

Month	Day	Name

Good Job!

Good Job Sticker

Draw a line from ➡ to ➡ to get through the zebra's stripes. Then, find the uppercase letter Z and trace it following the number order.

zebra

Let's Write Letters

To Parents: As an extension, ask your child to name each animal in the boxes at the bottom of the page. One at a time, say the name of the animal emphasizing the beginning sound, and then say, "Bear starts with the letter B," and so on.

Month	Day	Name

Good Job!

Good Job Sticker

Trace the letters W, w, X, x following the number order.

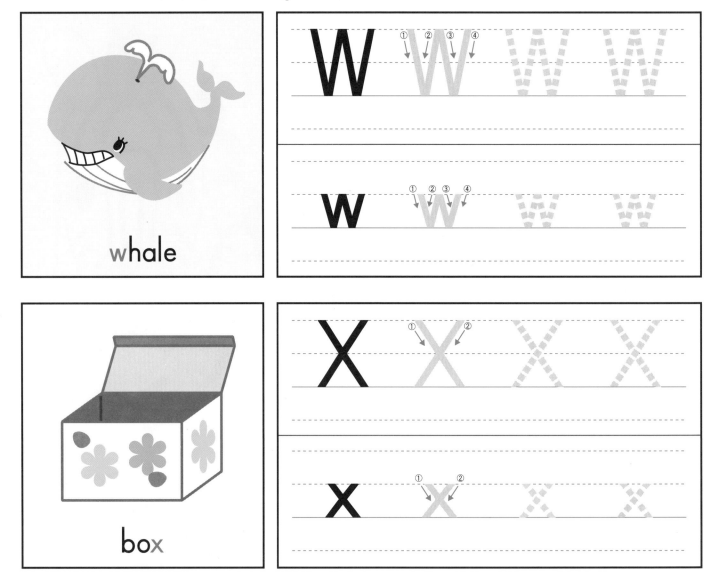

whale

box

Let's Write Letters

Good Job!

Good Job
Sticker

Trace the letters Y, y, Z, z following the number order.

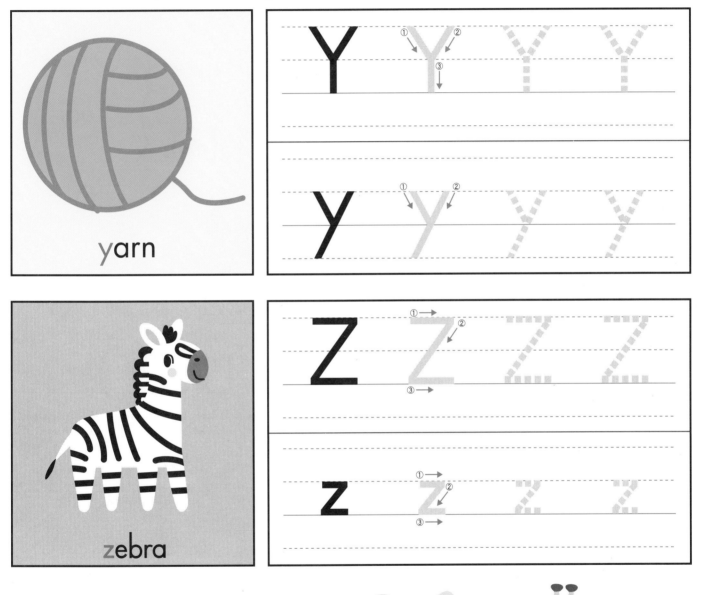

yarn

zebra

K   P   R   G

Let's Choose the Letters

Month	Day	Name

Trace the letter in each box. Then, ◯ the matching letter below.

alligator

(A , W)

bear

(U , B)

cat

(C , F)

deer

(Z , D)

Let's Choose the Letters

Month	Day	Name

Trace the letter in each box. Then, ◯ the matching letter below.

elephant

(E , T)

fish

(H , F)

giraffe

(C , G)

horse

(H , K)

Let's Match the Uppercase Letters

Month	Day	Name

Good Job!

Good Job Sticker

Find each letter from I through N in the picture. Draw a line between the matching letters in the picture and the box below.

I J K L M N

Let's Match the Uppercase Letters

Month	Day	Name

Good Job!

Good Job Sticker

Place each O, P, Q, R sticker on its match in the hippo's mouth.
After placing the stickers, color the picture with your favorite colors.

Let's Follow the Path

Month	Day	Name

Draw a line from ➡ to ➡ to help the worm through its burrow. Place the letter stickers matching each earthworm's shape along the way.

Let's Match the Uppercase Letters

Month	Day	Name

Trace the letters W, X, Y, and Z in each house. Then, find the cloud that matches each letter shape. Draw a line to connect the cloud with the house it matches.

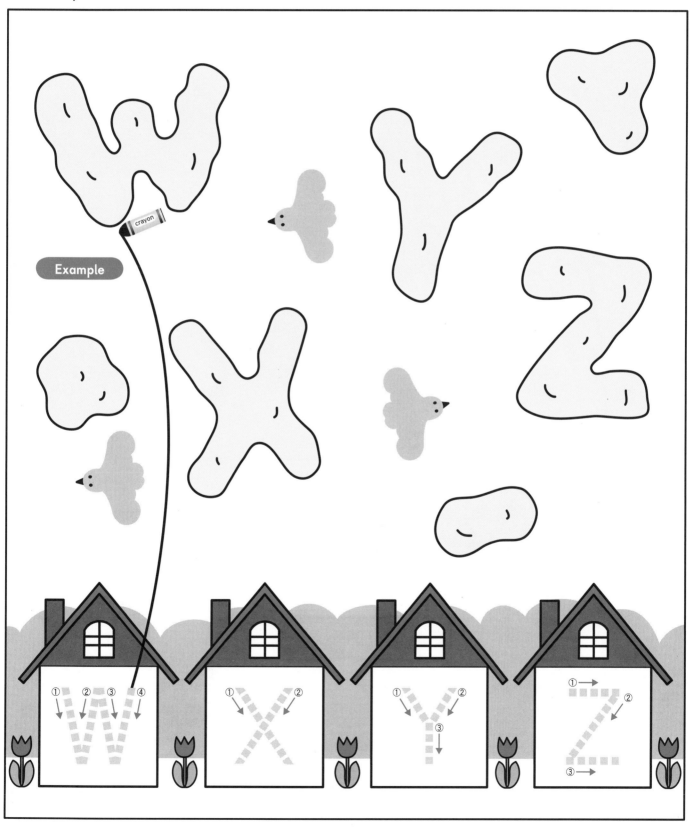

Example

Let's Find and Name the Objects

Find the shadow that matches each animal in the box. Draw a line to connect the animal with its shadow.

Example

panda

bird

sheep

mouse

koala

rabbit

Let's Find and Name the Objects

To Parents: All the objects inside the letter start with the letter D. Ask your child to name each object as he or she draws the line.

Good Job!

Good Job Sticker

Month	Day	Name

Find what is hidden in the letter D. Draw a line between each object in the letter and its match on the right.

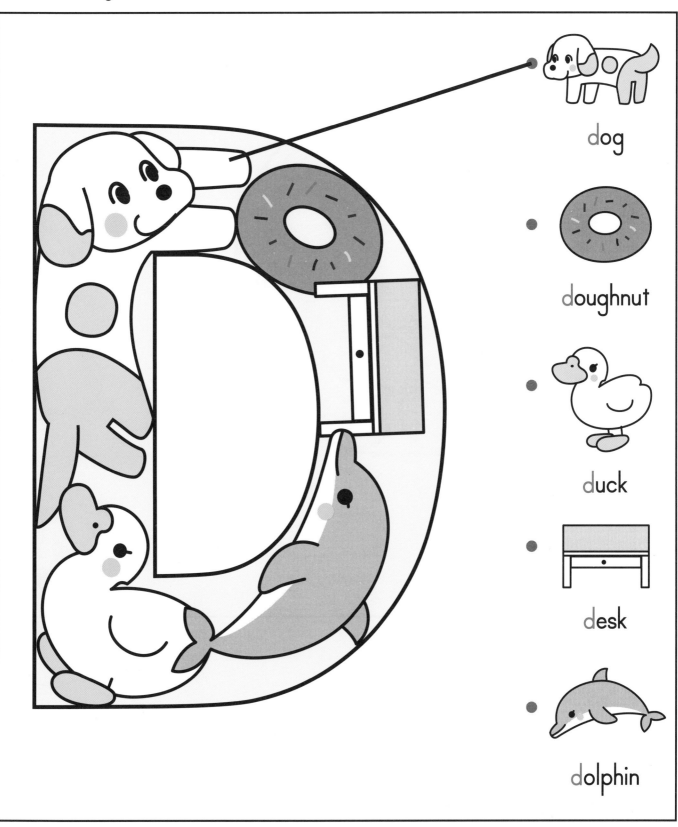

dog

doughnut

duck

desk

dolphin

Let's Find and Name the Objects

To Parents: All the objects inside the letter start with the letter P. Ask your child to name each object as he or she draws the line.

Month	Day	Name

Good Job!

Good Job Sticker

Find what is hidden in the letter P. Draw a line between each object in the letter and its match on the right.

pig

pencil

peach

panda

peanut

Let's Find and Name the Objects

To Parents: All the objects inside the letter start with the letter S. Ask your child to name each object as he or she draws the line.

Month	Day	Name

Good Job!

Good Job Sticker

Find what is hidden in the letter S. Draw a line between each object in the letter and its match on the right.

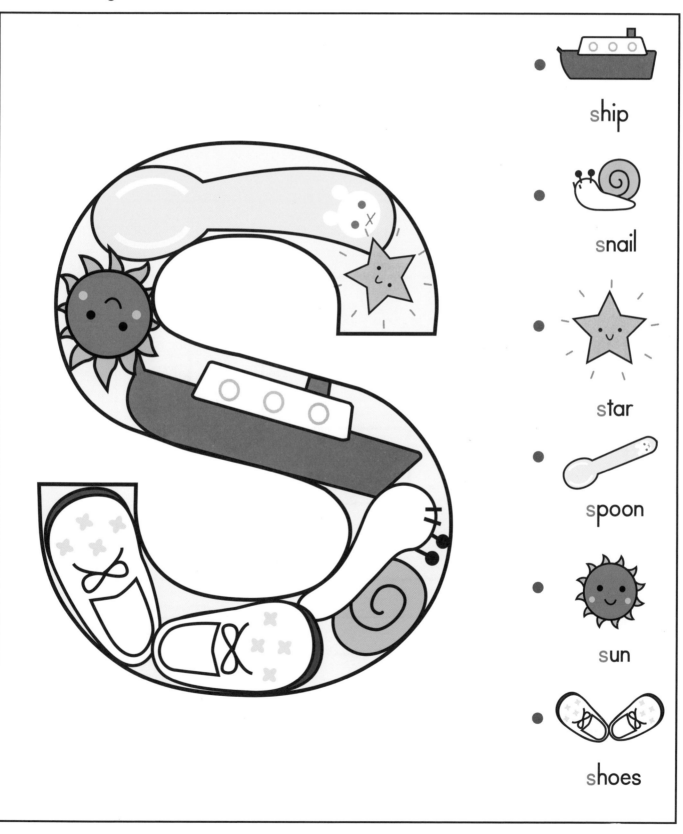

ship

snail

star

spoon

sun

shoes

Let's Follow the Path

To Parents: Ask your child to tell you where the fire truck is going (to the fire). Explain that the letters F, I, R, E together spell the word fire.

Month	Day	Name

Good Job!

Good Job Sticker

Draw a line from ➡ to ➡ by going through the letters F, I, R, E.

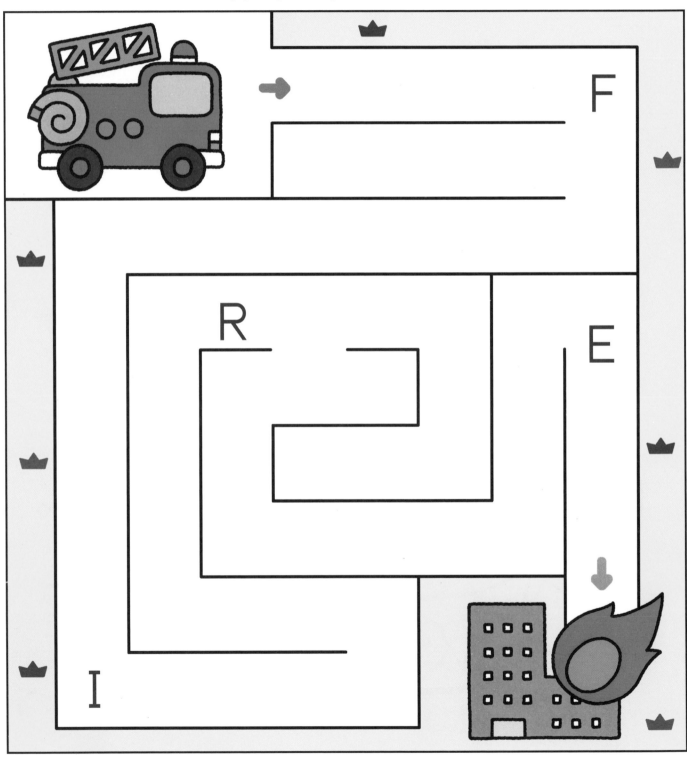

fire

Let's Match the Uppercase Letters

Month	Day	Name

Good Job!

Good Job Sticker

Connect the letter on each vehicle to its match on the community worker's sign.

Let's Match the Uppercase Letters

Month	Day	Name

Connect the letter on each train in the left column to its match on the right.

Let's Match Two Kinds of Letters

To Parents: Make sure your child understands that each pair of letters represents the same letter and sound.

Month	Day	Name

Good Job!

Good Job Sticker

Draw a line from ➡ to ➡ by matching the uppercase letters A, B, C, D, E with their lowercase letters. Place each lowercase letter sticker as you go through the maze.

Example

ant

ball

cake

A sticker

B sticker

C sticker

D sticker

E sticker

duck

egg

Let's Match Two Kinds of Letters

Month	Day	Name

Find the shadow that matches each object with the uppercase letters F, G, H, I, J. Draw a line between each match. Then, place the lowercase letter stickers on each shadow.

flower F

grape(s) G

hippo H

island I

jam J

sticker g

sticker h

sticker f

sticker j

sticker i

Let's Match Two Kinds of Letters

Month	Day	Name

Find out what each child caught fishing. Trace the lines to find matches to the uppercase letters K, L, M, N, and O. Then, place the lowercase letter stickers on what was caught.

Let's Match Two Kinds of Letters

Month	Day	Name

Draw a line from ➡ to ➡ to get from the peach to the umbrella. Place the lowercase letter stickers that match the uppercase letters P, Q, R, S, T, and U along the way.

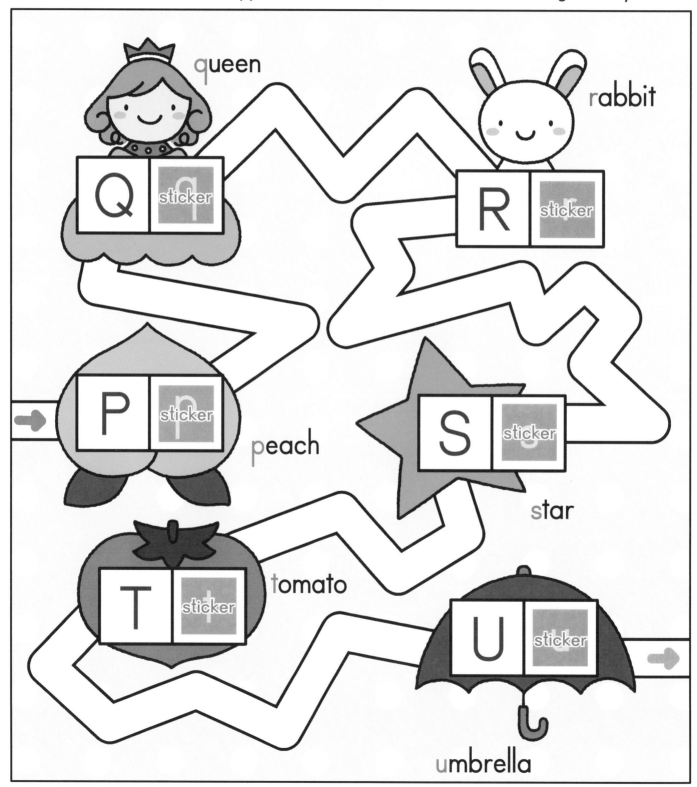

Let's Match Two Kinds of Letters

Month	Day	Name

Find the balloon each animal holds. Trace the lines to find matches to the uppercase letters V, W, X, Y, and Z. Then, place the lowercase letter stickers on each balloon.

Let's Write Letters

To Parents: The objects pictured with each letter have been introduced throughout the book. Ask your child to name each object as he or she writes the letters. Help your child name the object if he or she has difficulty remembering its name.

Month	Day	Name

Good Job!

Good Job Sticker

Write A, a, B, b, C, c following the number order.

A A A A

a a a a

B B B B

b b b b

C C C C

c c c c

Let's Write Letters

Month	Day	Name

Write D, d, E, e, F, f following the number order.

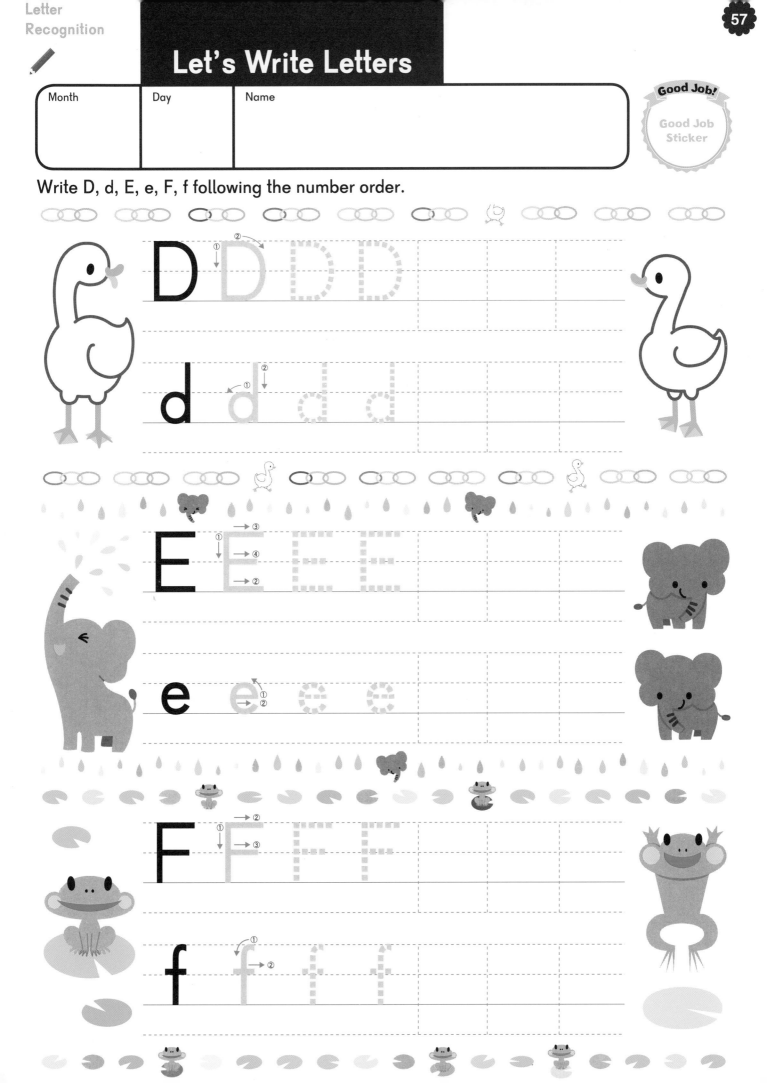

Let's Write Letters

Month	Day	Name

Write G, g, H, h, I, i following the number order.

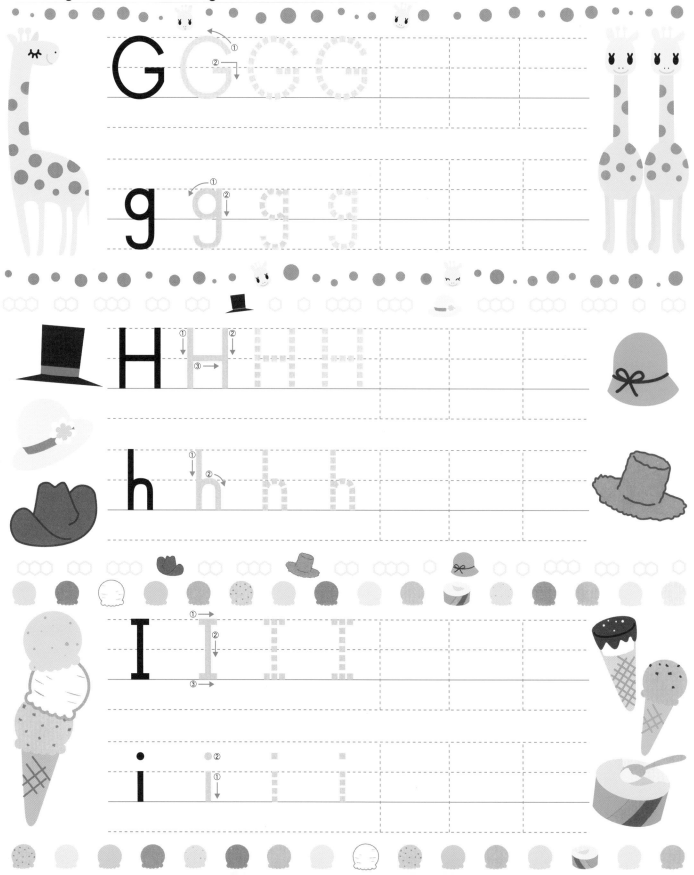

Let's Write Letters

Month	Day	Name

Write J, j, K, k, L, l following the number order.

J J J J J J J

j j j j

K K K K K

k k k k

L L L L

l l l

Let's Write Letters

Month	Day	Name

Write M, m, N, n, O, o following the number order.

Let's Write Letters

Month	Day	Name

Good Job!

Good Job Sticker

Write P, p, Q, q, R, r following the number order.

Let's Write Letters

Month	Day	Name

Good Job!

Good Job Sticker

Write S, s, T, t, U, u following the number order.

Let's Write Letters

Good Job!

Good Job
Sticker

Write V, v, W, w, X, x following the number order.

Let's Write Letters

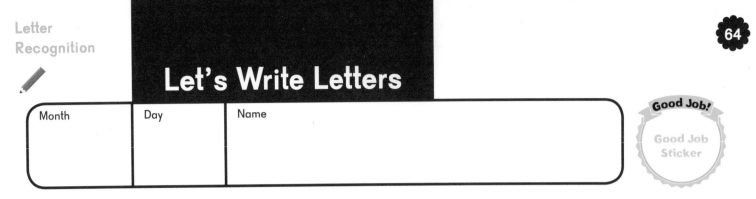

Month	Day	Name

Good Job!

Good Job
Sticker

Write Y, y, Z, z following the number order.